VOICES

NEW WELSH READER

New Welsh Reader
New Welsh Review Ltd
PO Box 170, Aberystwyth, SY23 1WZ
Telephone: 01970 628410
www.newwelshreview.com

Editor: Gwen Davies
editor@newwelshreview.com

Administration & Finance Officer:
Bronwen Williams
admin@newwelshreview.com

Marketing & Publicity Officer:
Edie Franklin
marketing@newwelshreview.com

Management Board:
Ali Anwar, Gwen Davies (Director),
Andrew Green (Director, Chair), Ruth
Killick, David Michael (Treasurer),
Matthew Francis, Emily Blewitt (Poetry
Subs Editor, Vice-Chair)

Aberystwyth University Partnership:
TK Quentin

**Sponsor of the New Welsh Writing
Awards:** RS Powell

Design: Ingleby Davies Design

Host: Aberystwyth University

Main images: Cover photographs ©
Griffiths family: (front), Lena Estella Littler,
(aunt of Elizabeth Griffiths) travelling
in Corsica, 1954, (front inside) parents
of Elizabeth in Llanelli on their wedding
day, 1958, (back inside) Lena in Paris,
1953, (back) Lena at Vaison-la-Romaine,
Provence, 1955. Contents page: 'Llanelli
Beach', illustration by Katherine Cleaver.

We acknowledge the financial support of
the Books Council of Wales and Creative
Wales for a New Audiences grant.

ISBN: 9781913830229
ISSN: 09542116

Views expressed in NWR are the authors'
own and do not necessarily reflect the
opinions of either editor or board.

The New Welsh Review Ltd publishes with
the financial support of the Books Council
of Wales, and is hosted by Aberystwyth
University's Department of English &
Creative Writing. The New Welsh Review
Ltd was established in 1988 by Academi
(now Literature Wales) and the Association
for Welsh Writing in English. *New Welsh
Reader* is New Welsh Review's print (and
digital) magazine for creative work. We
also publish monthly roundups of online
content, including reviews, comment and
poetry, and at least one book annually on
the New Welsh Rarebyte imprint, run a
writing competition (New Welsh Writing
Awards), and improve diversity in the UK
publishing industry by hosting student and
graduate work placements.

Mae croeso ichi ohebu â'r golygydd
yn Gymraeg.

Patrons: Belinda Humfrey, Owen Sheers

CYNGOR LLYFRAU CYMRU
BOOKS COUNCIL of WALES

Ariennir gan
Lywodraeth Cymru
Funded by
Welsh Government

PRIFYSGOL
ABERYSTWYTH
UNIVERSITY

Cyfnewidfa Lên Cymru
Wales Literature Exchange

LOVE POEM: RAIN

Like every hour, I'd thought of you on that cool summer evening, in
rain.

We were on our roof in Allahabad, our bodies
quietly sheltering dewdrops, like the leaves do after rain.

In a quiet moment, our lips had touched and the world had melted
like cotton candy, soft, on our tongue; like after it snows; like drops of
rain.

You'd looked at me, said that you loved me, said *I'm telling you I always
will; I want you like a river does banks, like it needs rain.*

I'm looking at you right now, my eyes loud like yours. I remember
you'd said that, until that moment, you'd never really liked rain.

We'd agreed that love is so much about learning. That winter doesn't
gather snow, but gives it a home; that memories are given a home by
rain.

Right now, I'm thinking about the times we shared a bit of whisky
in a peopled room, your glass full of coke and water, sweet like rain.

You say you remember all of this –

Jayant Kashyap has received nominations for the Pushcart Prize and the Best of the Net, and has published two pamphlets, and a zine, *Water* (Skear Zines, 2021). His work appears in *Poetry, Magma* and elsewhere. giantketchup.wordpress.com

NAMING HER HUNGERS

Land. Land above all. But also boats
and the fine men in them. Their nets,
their dreams, their greed or simple need.
She relishes the careless, the stranded,
day-trippers oblivious to tide,
cockle pickers, digging in her maw.
She loves a rig, a bridge, a pontoon,
a seawall or a lightship. But land,
land above all. Its crumbling edges,
the way it yields so suddenly, totally.
The way it gives itself, like coming home.

Rachael Davey is currently living and working on a Scottish seabird island.

LITTORAL

Barnacle. Limpet. Whelk.

                                                Surge

Wrack. Wreck. Rock.

     Sigh

Pebble. Pebble. Pebble.

                                                  Surge

Bone. Wing. Branch.

Sigh

Cobble, Boulder. Stone.

                                                Surge

Razor. Urchin. Crab.

     Sigh

Net. Plastic. Skull.

                                                Surge

Pebble. Pebble. Pebble.

Sigh

Sea mark. Sea wall. Sea mark.

                                                Surge

Boot. Cockle. Bottle.

Sigh

Pebble. Plastic. Pebble.

                                                Surge

Hssssh

                          Hssssh

                                                Hssssh

NEW WELSH WRITING AWARDS WINNER 2021

In pursuit of feeling 'sharply alive', Jasmine Donahaye roams Wales and beyond, undoing old lessons and confronting fear. Sometimes bristling, always ethical, Birdsplaining upends familiar ways of seeing the natural world.

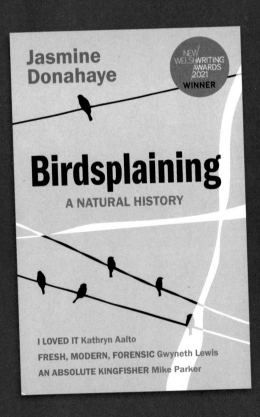

Jasmine Donahaye

NEW WELSH WRITING AWARDS 2021 WINNER

Birdsplaining
A NATURAL HISTORY

I LOVED IT Kathryn Aalto
FRESH, MODERN, FORENSIC Gwyneth Lewis
AN ABSOLUTE KINGFISHER Mike Parker

'A BEAUTIFUL [ESSAY] COLLECTION WHERE THE NONHUMAN APPEARS AS A CLOSE NEIGHBOUR.... [IT] SEARCHES FOR HOPE AND RESILIENCE IN TIMES OF RISK
New Welsh Reader

'CREATES ITS OWN ECOLOGICAL NICHE'
Caught by the River

'BRIDGES THE VERY GAP [IN NATURE WRITING] THAT [IT] IDENTIFIES'
The Welsh Agenda

'SUPERB... BY TURNS MOVING, FUNNY, ILLUMINATING... AND... THOUGHT-PROVOKING'
GoodReads

Paperback £9.99: *https://amzn.to/3Uc7RL6*
Epub £5.59: *https://amzn.to/3SzflGS*

NEW
WELSH WRITING
AWARDS
2021
WINNER

FEATURED AT FESTIVALS
INCLUDING OXFORD, HAY
AND THE EDINBURGH
INTERNATIONAL BOOK FESTIVAL!

LAST TOUR DATE IN 2023!
Kendal Mountain Festival, Saturday 18 November, 12.15pm
Town Hall Chambers, Kendal, Cumbria

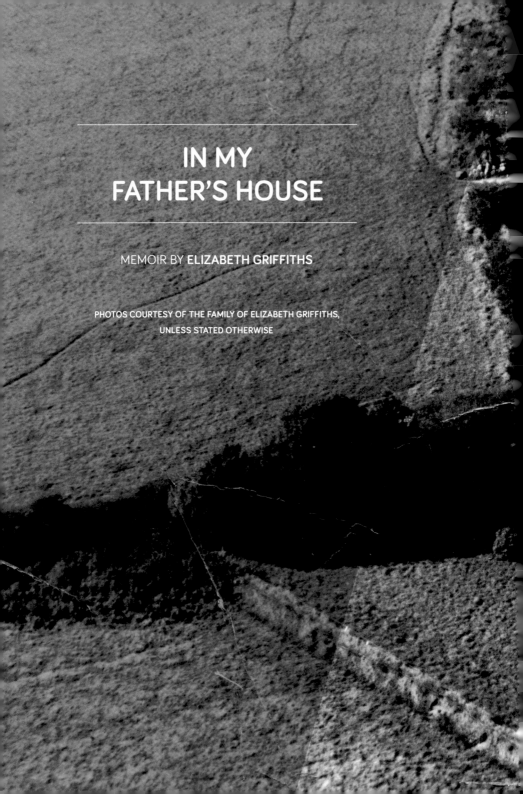

IN MY
FATHER'S HOUSE

MEMOIR BY **ELIZABETH GRIFFITHS**

An aerial view of the first rectory of the writer's family, in the Preseli hills, where her twin sisters were born.

WHEN I WAS YOUNG IT WASN'T THE HOUSES WE LIVED IN THAT PREOCCUPIED my father, but Houses of God. Each of the small country churches he looked after became, for a while, a labour of love. If he dashed home looking dishevelled and dirty, his hair almost white with dust, we knew that Dad had been 'mending the church'. If we heard hammering inside the building as we passed, we imagined him hacking great chunks of green-streaked plaster off the walls prior to repairing the stonework himself, as best he could.

Once I went back to the first church where he was rector in a small village in the Preseli hills and by chance met a parishioner who remembered him and showed me part of the chancel wall which he had repointed nearly fifty years ago. It had remained untouched ever since. 'He did a good job,' the parishioner had said, smiling. And it made me smile too, that rather than a plaque or a name on a board, the wall itself was a kind of memorial to him.

My father tackled these building projects as soon as we moved to a new parish, but before long they fizzled out, probably for lack of time and money as well as enthusiasm. He was always at his most energised in the first months after a move, and these were the best times for our family. Dad was happy then, his most inspiring self, full of ideas and rushing off, morning to night. To my sisters and I he appeared 'dashing' in more senses than one. He was taller and younger than other priests we knew, with dark, almost black hair, and the kind of looks that reminded us of film stars in the Dirk Bogarde mould. At supper he would say what a perfect parish he had, what a wonderful house. We didn't know how lucky we were.

'Nine months,' my mother told me later. 'That's how long it used to last.'

It was she who bore the labour of looking after the cavernous rectories and vicarages that came with the churches. If my father was around, we would more often hear him rather than see him: the swift

The family's second Pembrokeshire rectory, pictured in the 1890s, facing north-east (the east wing shown behind trees had been demolished by the time they lived there in the mid 1960s). Photo courtesy of Chancellor Geoffrey Morris.

flip-flap of his black cassock beating like a wing through the house as he flew in or out, or made a beeline for the study, his refuge from family and parish life.

'I don't want to hear a single sound!' he would plead on 'sermon day' – Saturday – even if we weren't making a squeak.

I was only just old enough to remember our first rectory and his study there, a large formal, gracious room, overlooking lawns at the front. It set a pattern for all the studies to come: there was a wide leather-topped desk and ample wooden chair with curved arms, both acquired at antiques auctions. Shelves full of history and theology books assiduously collected since university. Brass candlesticks on the mantelpiece, a large wooden crucifix above. The faint background odour of pipe tobacco, both raw and sweet. Later, a piano on which I sometimes used to hear

him play, softly and slowly, long after our bedtime, the melodious 'Jesu, Joy of Man's Desiring'.

It was in that first study, he told me, that he heard some words which must have made a impression on him, because he would repeat them occasionally throughout his life, savouring each word of the original Welsh. They were spoken by a well-respected chapel minister, who had just been given a big promotion. My father was in the middle of offering his congratulations when the minister interrupted, laid a hand on his arm and said, '*Ydw, rwy'n symud, Kenneth bach, ond y cyfeiriad sy'n bwysig.*' (Yes I'm moving, Kenneth bach, but it's the direction that's important.)

My mother told me that my father couldn't bear the sound of babies crying, that it drove him out of the house when we were small. Or if he had to stay in, she would find ways to take us out of earshot. As the first-born, I was the most trouble to him, and it was lucky that the spring and summer were fine that year, my mother said, because she could spend hours nursing me at the far end of the garden.

Years later, I tried to imagine what my father had been like before I could remember him, when I was that bawling newborn he wanted to escape from. I began writing a scenario inspired – I knew not quite why – by the line *it's the direction that's important*, in which I pictured him bursting into the kitchen, his cassock flailing around his calves: *For crying out loud, why won't that child stop?* While my mother, cradling me by the Rayburn, simply looked at him as if she had neither the energy nor will to answer.

'*The stove's gone out,*' she said. '*It's cold.*'

'*What?*' The rector strode across and rattled the hatch open. '*How could you have let that happen? After I spent nearly an hour this morning getting it lit!*'

He was incredulous, practically shaking with frustration, while she continued to look at him. The baby's screaming tore the air above their heads.

Sitting room of the family's first rectory in the Preseli hills in 1961: Elizabeth's twin sisters as babies, her in the middle and her young parents behind.

'Well there's nothing I can do about it now. I'm late for Ebbw Roberts' funeral as it is.'

And pretending he hadn't seen the tears in her eyes, he turned on his heel and marched from the room, shutting the door soundly behind him.

In the chilly hallway, he flung on his long black clerical cloak and fastened its ornate brass clasp, felt the thick engulfing folds settle around him. He hesitated in the gloom, next to the baby's pram, wondering whether to go back into the kitchen, where the child was still emitting a constant grizzle. He decided to leave by the front door.

Out of the house he felt he had been released – could breathe again. Striding down the driveway, he sensed an expectancy in the air such as you get before snow, or before a special season like Christmas. A breeze was stirring the huge rhododendron bushes on each side of the drive. He liked those bushes – exotic; lush, they were, in unforgiving hill country like this where the wind raked the bare stone-covered mountains and land was grazed to the bone.

The rectory, standing all on its own, was quickly lost to sight as the road dipped down to the village beneath a dark bower of trees. It was like walking into night. The wind, picking up, rustled the high branches overhead, rooks flapped and cawed above the tree tops, and beneath his cape the rector felt his chest swell excitably with a rising sensation – the sensation of his own rise still to come.

Walking swiftly, cloak and cassock flowing behind him, he entered the village feeling strong and calm. Ebbw Roberts had been a staunch Methodist, so he had no demanding duties at the funeral that afternoon, only a Bible reading to give in English. He was in no doubt that his readings in Welsh would soon be just as fluent if he carried on practising. 'I can't understand your preaching, rector, your Welsh is too good for me,' one of the congregation commented on his sermon last Sunday.

The houses lining the roadside were simple enough: a few cottages, a bungalow or two, and here and there a farmhouse with outbuildings. But they had a pleasant look about them, unlike the look of the miners' houses where he came from, which huddled in the shadow of the slag heaps as if they had no roots there, no right to exist.

Elizabeth's parents on a Butlins family holiday gifted to them by the bishop, circa 1964.

He was suddenly seized with a passion for the village – his parish, his domain. He was passing the church now, an ancient country church, quite small and plain. He planned after Christmas to set about restoring it with his own hands, so that in eighteen months', two years' time – when new challenges might well be within his sights: a fast promotion perhaps, a new, bigger parish – he would leave this church with his mark upon it.

He was twenty-five and had it all ahead of him.

***

The 'good' things in Granny's house, as we called it, belonged to my father's sister, his elder by five years, and were collected in the sitting room. My aunt's piano, her books and record collection, and rows of white-painted shelves she'd had made specially to hold the mementos she brought back while working as a secretary and personal assistant, first at the Foreign Office in London, then for the United Nations in Geneva and Libya. There was also one thing of Grandpa's in the room, a silver cup he had won for gardening [....] Like my father, my aunt moved away as a young woman to live and work in places very different from their childhood home, in the street of Ger-yr-afon. She too had a sensibility, a sensitivity that seemed to set her apart from her home environment. In company they were both well spoken, well-mannered, careful with their appearance. Even when I was young, I had a strange feeling that they had somehow ended up in the wrong place. Neither would ever have imagined spending their lives in Ger-yr-afon, yet the mark made on them by years of close living in that one small community went deep.

You could hear it in their voices as they talked over news of their near contemporaries who had lived in that same street and had gone on to do well, usually in academia or professions like medicine or the

Elizabeth's aunt in the Libyan desert while working for the UN, 1957. Her aunt's travels in France, between 1953 and 1955, are depicted on our covers.

Church. In fact, it really was quite surprising, my father observed later in life, how many people from the neighbourhood of Ger-yr-afon *did* do well, a few becoming widely known, even famous, in their fields.

I once saw a 1950s photo, now lost to me, of my father on holiday in Geneva as a guest of my aunt. They are pictured before a grand colonnaded building – the palatial United Nations Office in Geneva, I believe. My father is leaning one arm on a parapet behind him, looking sideways towards his sister, who is almost as tall and slim as he is. Their poses are relaxed, willowy; almost languid. It's a fine day in summer most likely: my aunt is in a short-sleeved two-piece, my father in brilliant white shirt sleeves.

I've since hunted high and low for that black-and-white snap taken in Switzerland, but to no avail. So why has this particular image stayed with me? Perhaps because there, in front of the Palais des Nations, beside Lake Geneva, my father and his sister look as if they have the world at their feet.

Elizabeth Griffiths lives in Pembrokeshire, where she grew up. She studied at St David's University College, Lampeter, and trained as a journalist on the *Barry and District News* in what was then South Glamorgan. Several of her short stories have appeared in Welsh publications, including Parthian Books' anthology of New Welsh Short Fiction, *Mama's Baby (Papa's Maybe)*. She worked for many years in the visual arts, which involved writing about and assisting with painting exhibitions and sculpture installations. In 2018, she completed a Creative Writing MA at Swansea University. Her entry, 'In My Father's House', was placed second in the New Welsh Writing Awards 2023 Rheidol Prize for Prose with a Welsh Setting this summer, gaining for Elizabeth a stay at Nant, a self-catering retreat on the site of Tŷ Newydd.

Elizabeth's parents (centre) outside their third Pembrokeshire vicarage circa 1974, with her on the right and her sister Esther on the left.

SIGN UP!

Our new website can be browsed by category, theme tag or title and is now a one-stop shop for our ePub formats and fully searchable digital archive, books, offers & more. New-look digital editions are fully searchable, have page-turning feature and include complete text to speech (TTS) element as standard.

newwelshreview.com

Emmy Hennings.

NEW WELSH READER

#134 ESSAYS, MEMOIR, STORIES, POETRY

Emmy Hennings: Conversions
Katie Jones on a poet, performer, Dadaist and sex worker.

Crumbs Ghost story by JL George.

REVIEWS, COMMENT, POETRY

Roger Reeves.

Lairs
Judy Brown

Poems on anger and friendship by Dylan McNulty-Holmes, and on memory and ageing by Robert Benz.

Essay collection review *Dark Days: Fugitive Essays by Roger Reeves.* Elaine Margolin on the New Jersey poet's latest book, about ecstacy as a tool of activism in the #BlackLivesMatter movement.

Nonfiction/nature/travel review *Sarn Helen: A Journey Through Wales, Past, Present and Future* by Tom Bullough. Solly Hardwick is impressed by this journey into a past suffused with myth and memory, as well as a present threatened by ecological disaster.

Poetry review *Lairs* by Judy Brown. Victoria MacKenzie finds that this collection on maths and uncertainty offers an unsettling but invigorating perspective on our own strange and complex world.

Live interviews Gwen Davies talks to Jasmine Donahaye and Eluned Gramich about mountains, flowers and domestic violence at Palas Print bookshop, Caernarfon (video), and about skating, Nemesis and colonial willy waving with Jasmine, Rachel Hewitt and Jay Griffiths at Hay Festival (audio).

THE KING OF SWANSEA

NONFICTION AND ILLUSTRATIONS BY
KATHERINE CLEAVER

Map of Vernon House,
Briton Ferry.

DURING THE 1800S, EVERY COUNTY HAD TO HAVE A SO-CALLED 'LUNATIC asylum', Glamorgan included, but the county was too poor to build one, so they 'rented' space from the private asylum in Briton Ferry, Vernon House. The house itself was a converted mansion and had not been designed as an 'asylum'. Katherine's research for her creative nonfiction book, 'The King of Swansea', is centred around eight private patients that were committed by their families between 1850 and 1880. These were ordinary middle-class people who suffered different mental illnesses. Some of their families appear to have been reluctant, and others more keen, to have their family members declared insane, yet in either case, their relatives ended up at Vernon House. Her book and accompanying illustrations bring to life the house and people, their lost voices and their fate, as well as informing the reader about early care for the mentally ill. What follows is a fictionalised account of one patient, Tom, prior to his forced incarceration at Vernon House.

16 March 1846

Tom likes the horses, and they like him. The smell of them in the early morning as the sun is climbing makes him feel like he is home. He doesn't feel the cold so much in the room above the stables. He had only been helping the groom a week when he was moved out of the house and above the horses. Those first few nights were so incredibly cold. Tom had lain under the two blankets he had been given and felt the straw digging in from his mattress. He was happy that the straw was fresh. The smell clean and natural, not like the damp wool that had filled his old mattress. He missed the warmth that seeped from the floors below and the chimney breast, but he did not miss the damp and the walls. So many walls. All grey with untreated stone. The front of the house was all white and wonderful. But that was a lie. Behind the scenes it was drab, grey and damp.

In the stables it was different. The horses did not lie. If they were happy, they told you; angry, then they bit. Tom understood them. He didn't understand those in the house. Not really and not anymore.

We have each other, his wife says, twirling around the room that is now his. The dress she wears is white with flowers over it, daisies, and as she spins it rises in a most unseemly manner. Tom doesn't mind though. Grass flows around her feet, despite the fact they stand on a wooden floor and flowers bloom with every musical note of her laughter. He sits on the bed with its straw mattress and thin blankets and smiles as she dances.

He could be anywhere watching his wife dance; he isn't in a hovel above a stable. He sits on the same grass she dances on, and it isn't Jack Frost that nips at his cheeks, but the sun that warms them.

'We will always have each other,' he says, and for a moment he smells wood smoke and sees worn hands, female hands. His mother? He looks away from the sun and for a second sees the way his own hands are red raw from the cold and feels how his bones can be seen a little more prominently than normal.

Silly, his wife says, softly stroking his cheek. *I will always be here. They can't take you from me.*

Tom looks into the eyes of his wife and is glad that they are the same colour as his mother's. Except where she was tired and sad, she is bright and alive.

'No more sadness,' he says.

Never, after all I married the king of Swansea. How can I be sad?

'Thomas?'

A voice filters through from below. A few horses stamp their feet but don't show they are in distress. Tom gets up and walks toward the narrow stairs.

'Hello?'

'Thomas, can you come down here?' the voice sounds like the lord, but Tom hasn't heard him since he moved to the stables.

Slipping down the stairs Tom stands for a second watching the lord stroke the satin soft nose of the lead horse. The stallion is standing still

Melancholia due to excessive smoothing and shirt changing, dementia cause unknown, melancholia due to money matters, chronic mania caused by religious monomania, chronic mania caused by a house dispute, mania paralysis cause unknown, general paralysis caused by vexation, melancholia cause unknown, mania with paralysis cause by excessive venery, melancholia with suicidal tenancies

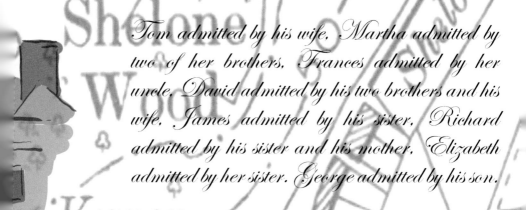

Tom admitted by his wife, Martha admitted by two of her brothers, Frances admitted by her uncle, David admitted by his two brothers and his wife, James admitted by his sister, Richard admitted by his sister and his mother, Elizabeth admitted by her sister, George admitted by his son.

and lowering his head, allowing himself to be touched. Tom knows that if Hercules decided to not be touched there was little that could be done to bend his will. But the horse is standing there as docile as a lamb, allowing the man who has control over his life and death to stroke his nose.

The lord revels in the soft nose of his favourite horse. It was his father who had placed him on his first horse, and it was his father who had bred Hercules. The lord had been at the birth.

Tom coughs a little.

The lord starts and turns to the man who he had liked as a boy.

'Thomas,' he says. 'We have things to discuss.'

Tom nods but doesn't move. His face is impassive and his eyes blank. The lord finds this the worst. It is almost as if he can see the lunacy.

'I had hoped that by moving out here you would see your mistakes and make amends.'

'I won't give her up,' Tom says.

The lord sighs and gives a slight nod. 'I know.'

There is a moment of silence as the horse snickers and leans his head into the lord's chest. Tom expects him to push the animal away and tut at the hairs on his suit, but instead he pats the horse's cheek.

'I am sorry,' Tom says, and he means it. He understands that in some way he is failing the man in front of him, but he cannot grasp how. He had thought it was his wife, but the whole thing seems very extreme for an unplanned marriage. As a king, he does not agree with how the lord is running things. He cannot see the error that would mean this sort of banishment.

'I know you are, but I also know you don't truly understand what is going on.'

Silence again.

Previous pages: 'Living with Vernon' won the Research as Art prize at Swansea University in 2019, a competition providing a platform for students, researchers and university staff to convey the importance of their research through the medium of art.

'Do you remember coming here?' the lord asks.

'Of course.'

'How we supported and looked after you?'

Tom remembers sleeping in the embers near the fire and how the cook would kick him. He was warmer and there had been more food, but he had missed the soft touch of his mother and the fact she had sung all the time. That had hurt worse. He would have woken to her voice and gone to sleep with it. But suddenly they were gone, as if they had never been.

'It was an act of kindness that we gave you.'

Tom gives a tiny nod of his head. Perhaps it had been. But it had also been the cruellest thing that had happened to him.

'You repay us by....' The lord sighs. 'Except I have spoken to the local doctor, and he has expressed concerns regarding your competence. I must agree with him.'

Tom says nothing.

The lord isn't facing Tom; instead, he is petting the horse. The conversation appears to be between them: Tom is merely an observer.

'At first, I was worried that your illness was nothing more than ill manners. Then my son started to bring me tales. How you spoke when no one was there, and you would not move for hours. That unless you were given an explicit order you did nothing. I spoke to the steward, and he said that you were good at your work but lacked the ability to initiate anything. It seemed strange to us both. You were moved about the house and every work you did you did it well.' He sighs and shakes his head. 'But something was wrong. I understood that you had slipped into lunacy from the blood on your hand. That was not normal.'

Tom opens his left hand and sees the cuts made by his own fingernails. They resemble the face of a woman, and he smiles down at his wife. She smiles back.

'That is when I started to worry your affliction could be catching. You were moved here in order to keep my wife and child away from you.'

Vernon House, Briton Ferry, in the 1880s.

Tom looks up and the lord is staring at him.

'In a couple of days, you will be sent to a place that can help you. But you will be on your own. Agree with me that there is nothing there, that you have no wife, and perhaps you can stay. But you must agree.'

'I am married,' Tom says. He watches as the man in front of him sighs and turns away, walking out of the stable, toward the house that used to be home. He feels the hand of his wife slip into his and he squeezes it slightly.

He doesn't understand, she says.

'No, he doesn't.'

18 March 1846

Today is the day, Tom's wife says as he wakes.

He says nothing but watches the condensation of his breath in the cold air.

Don't be sad.

Tom considers this. Is he sad to be leaving the stable, its thin blankets and cold? No, although the possibility of getting a worse situation....

Don't think like that.

He smiles but says nothing. He knows he doesn't really have to. His wife can read his thoughts, although he normally prefers to talk to her aloud. Looking at the one wooden bed made from scrap wood and slats, he wonders what he ought to take with him. The blanket? Perhaps, but what did he own?

Even the clothes on his back were technically the property of the lord. He had lost any original possession that he had come with. Even the small animal toy his mother had made him had been thrown in the fire. His eight-year-old self had watched it burn, the flames stealing the last thing that would remind him of home.

The cook had fallen over the small animal that had sort of looked like a dog. Tom couldn't remember what it had meant to be, had forgotten the name that he gave it, but he did remember the smell. The last thing that had reminded him of his mother. The soft animal had smelt like home. The day it had been burned had been the day that he had lost the last of the things that spoke to him of home. After that everything had been provided for him. He had money, a little, but the uniform he wore had to be bought, then extra food.

'Should I have sent it home?' he asks.

What?

'The money I had.'

In the tin?

Tom nods. His wife looks pensive for a moment.

Where is the tin?

Tom shrugs. When he was moved over, the tin had been missing. But his stuff had been brought by another.

'We are moving you,' a cheery voice had said.

Tom shakes his head and sighs. He should have known that there was something amiss. The servant in question was never cheerful.

'He took it,' Tom tells his wife as he picks up the blanket and wraps it around his shoulders. The fabric is so thin that he can almost see through it.

It will get better, she says.

He says nothing and wishes that he could feel his wife's optimism. The cold makes his nose and throat hurt. Sniffing, he can almost taste the sickness that he knows is there. Hovering in the background.

It will be fine. The softest of touches passes across his hand. Tom watches the blanket shift in the breeze and sighs. Slowly he stands, wincing as his knees twinge. He needs to get out of here, go somewhere better. His body feels far older than his twenty-five years.

Below he hears a carriage pull up. Briefly he considers fighting. Disobeying the lord and his own feelings. Showing that he is merely a scared man rather than a king. For that is what he is, a king.

As I am your queen?

Tom smiles and sees his wife, hand resting on his, her smooth skin and his roughness.

'Always,' he says.

Bridgend cyclists relax with medals and cups in front of a delapidated and empty Vernon House, Briton Ferry.

Katherine Cleaver is a disabled autistic Anglo-Indian writer who is currently finishing her PhD with Swansea University. She is predominately a creative nonfiction writer who specialises in history, especially within Wales. For her PhD , she is looking into the lives of ordinary people who found themselves incarcerated in the Briton Ferry Insane Asylum, Vernon House. She has had a memoir piece published by Parthian in *Just So You Know*, and with Honno in *Painting the Beauty Queens Orange*. The creative nonfiction entry, 'The King of Swansea', from which this is an extract, was highly commended in the New Welsh Writing Awards 2023 Rheidol Prize for Prose with a Welsh Theme or Setting, judged by Gwen Davies at a ceremony at Hay Festival this summer. katemurray.co.uk/

INVISIBILITY

NOVELLA PREVIEW BY **MARK BLAYNEY**

WE START WITH A ROBBERY. THE MONEY IS STOLEN FROM RUIZ, A LIVESTOCK trader with a large home on the main street. By the island's standards his house is huge. The money could be anywhere. Under floorboards is usual. But which floorboards? Upstairs, nearest the bedrooms, might be logical. There is a strongbox, in an office, but this strongbox is not touched, and the door to the office remains closed.

The intruder knows that the room he wants is on the ground floor, in the right-hand third of rooms. Three floorboards need to be levered up to get to the trunk, because it has been lowered in and then shoved as far as can be pushed.

It might have taken weeks for Ruiz to discover the theft were it not for the fact that, as he crosses the space to the study, the floor creaks under his foot. Ruiz looks down. The thief has done a professional job, slotting the boards neatly back into place and escaping without leaving any visible traces. Without even kneeling to examine the wood, Ruiz knows what has happened. He feels a draining of saliva in his throat, a coldness in his fingers, a kind of freeze, a paralysis, rapidly followed by the hot, righteous anger of being a victim.

He still doesn't lift the boards. His eye moves across the floor to the window. There are two tell-tale scratch marks on the white sill, where the thief has jumped through, rested the trunk for a second and then heaved it after him.

Find the trunk and we get the money back, Ruiz thinks. Or, will he have hacked it open under cover of trees, away from the house where it won't matter about making noise? These thoughts, and other less savoury ones, tumble through Ruiz's mind as now he gets on his knees and runs his finger round the edge of the floorboard, and it lifts too easily under his nail.

When Ruiz's servants hear his cries and rush in, they think he has injured himself. They attempt to help and he shouts, yelling at them to get off, what are they doing. 'Get the governor,' he says, and then remembers that the governor is no longer the governor, it is some English brute who prowls about and wears his provocative red uniform as if it is made with the blood of his victims. 'No, don't get the governor,' he amends, and his servants wonder if he is well. He shouts, yes! – but he is rarely indecisive.

'I have been robbed,' he explains, realising with a tsk of annoyance at himself that the servants now know where his hiding place was. If he gets the trunk back, he will have to think of a new solution. Another tsk of self-condemnation: it will be harder to identify if any of the servants was the culprit. Or told the culprit.

Slow down, he tells himself: say nothing. They also now know that the strongroom is a chimera. That was supposed to be the place, were anyone to attack his wealth, that they would approach. Ostentatiously built into a cupboard, to blindside those who would see him ill. A whole new arrangement will have to be found. Perhaps it would be simpler to sack all his staff and start again.

He taps his teeth. 'Yes,' he says, back to his calm self now. 'Do go and get the governor.' It would be good to build relations with the man, regardless of the jumped-up country he comes from.

Both servants look at him as if he is mad then nod and hurry, moving backwards, not wanting to turn on him.

Ruiz goes to the bedroom and stares at Luisa, who is asleep. She has taken to afternoon naps lately; he wonders if she is pregnant. When he leans in, she does not stir.

'Luisa,' he says. When he rattles her shoulder, she opens her eyes and stares at him.

Nobody wants to be brought to the governor. Everyone knows the stories – of his brutality, of his ruling as if we are under military law. But if you have done nothing wrong, you have nothing to fear. Have you? Speak truth, and what harm can befall you?

Government House is not as we might expect. It is more like a fort than a home. The contrast with Ruiz's expansive residence could not be greater. Here are plain walls, unpolished floors, shutters kept open even at the peak of the day so that blinding white oblongs appear on the wall's blueish plaster. Perhaps this is the way the governor likes it; perhaps it helps him think like a soldier; perhaps he knows no other way of behaving.

A functional wood desk, its joints aching in the heat. A chair which bends in similar protest. A man in a stiff collar and heavy coat is not used to humidity and it makes him irritable, but it would not occur to him to remove the collar or wear something lighter. He has been here four years and would not admit that he still struggles in the temperature. Never reveal a fault or a weakness. Threads would unravel, possibly to the point of anarchy.

Luisa is shown into the room and looks about uncertainly. There are two pictures on the wall, both of fat men with long white hair and badges. The woman who showed her in beats a fast retreat, closing the door so Luisa stands alone in front of the governor.

'Well. Your name?' Unexpectedly, the governor speaks perfect Spanish.

'Luisa Calderón.'

'Very good.' He makes a note on the ledger, then looks up. 'You are accused of the theft of a substantial sum of money from your master's house.'

She nods. His eyes widen.

'You admit the offence?'

'No.' The nod was to show that she understood the accusation.

'You were there at the time?'

'No.'

'But you gave the information. That enabled the theft.'

'I was not there.'

'You were there.'

'No.'

The girl blinks. What is she: thirteen or fourteen, perhaps. Children of that age can deceive with perfection. His eldest son, one of four, is five now and it is astounding, his ability to lie, his insouciance, his bare-facedness. Catch him with a hand stained red with fruit and the boy will swear he has not eaten since breakfast.

Someone in the household must have told the thief where the money was kept. Ruiz has squarely accused the girl, but it is unclear why he is so convinced of her guilt. He doesn't seem to think she took the money, but appears more concerned that Luisa is put in front of him than the actual thief.

'You gave the information, that gave the felon,' he rifles about for piece of paper, 'the accused... what's the man's name... the knowledge he needed, to find the money.'

The absent-mindedness is an act: he hopes that the name might spill from her.

'I did not do that.'

The governor taps the ledger and settles back in his seat. 'The money was taken. There was no one else in the house. Señor Ruiz has accused you. You helped Gonzalez,' no advantage in concealing the name now, 'you helped Gonzalez take the money.'

'I was not there,' she repeats, 'and I did not take the money.'

'You said where the money was.'

Now Luisa shrugs, helpless.

'Admit it.'

'I cannot.'

The governor stands, keeps talking as he heads to the door. Casually: 'You sleep with Señor Ruiz, don't you? You are his whore?'

The girl squares her shoulders. 'No.'

The governor opens the door and shouts, 'In here!' The woman Bella scuttles in. She's terrified, Luisa thinks, not simply a scuttler by nature, and I would be terrified of the man too, were I in his employ. The governor whispers and the woman nods. Luisa is taken aside and the same questions are asked by Bella. She is not sure what the motive is, unless perhaps the governor thinks that a woman doing the asking might persuade her to say more.

The governor makes a show of leaving the room for a few moments, then returns. The answers are predictably unhelpful. 'The girl knows nothing about it, sir. She was somewhere else.'

'Ask whether she is Ruiz's prostitute.'

The woman balks, affronted.

'When did you become involved with Señor Ruiz?'

Luisa shrugs. 'Complicated.'

He ignores the insolence. Bella, seeing a clear run to the door when the governor's eyes are not on her, dashes out. He shakes his head. Luisa feels momentarily sorry for him, having to impose order when no one is inclined to think the way he does.

'I was taken into the house aged eleven,' she says. 'I serve.'

'You are a slave?'

She shakes her head. 'Free.'

'And you sleep with him.'

'He has promised he will marry me.'

The governor snorts. Luisa waits.

'Very well. Get out.'

She doesn't move for a moment, and he roars at her, 'Get out!' He has a cracked, crackly voice, as if something is permanently lodged in his throat.

In the narrow lobby Bella comforts the girl, who shakes with fear.

'What will happen to me?'

'Go home. Nothing will happen to you.'

'How do you know?'

'Just go home. You will be safe.'

Bella can see that Luisa does not believe her, and she is right not to. But what else can she say? The governor is impetuous, inconsistent. The best way to prevent anything happening is to lie low, wait for the storm to pass. If something more significant comes up today, he will forget all about her.

Although this sounds too hopeful, too optimistic, there are grounds for Bella to believe this. The governor has not been here long, relatively speaking. The invasion was unexpected and Bella understands that this is because Spain and England are now enemies. There is little sense to be made of this. A year earlier they were allies, united against the French. Bella doesn't know what has happened to change that situation but the fact is that the English have taken the island from Spain for reasons which, even if they were clear, would make little difference to the inhabitants.

The point is that this governor might be usurped next week. The Spanish might come back. Someone else might arrive – the Portuguese, the Dutch, the French, who knows? Yes, next week will probably be the same as this week –but then again, it may be entirely different. It does no harm to be optimistic.

Mark Blayney won the Somerset Maugham Award for his story books, *Two Kinds of Silence,* and is currently a Royal Literary Fellow based at Cardiff University. His entry 'Invisibility', a fictionalised account of the life of Thomas Picton (previewed above), won the New Welsh Writing Awards 2023 Rheidol Prize for Prose with a Welsh theme or setting, which was presented at Hay Festival this summer. The entry will now be developed, with judge and editor Gwen Davies, into a book for publication on the magazine's New Welsh Rarebyte imprint. His previous story collection, *Doppelgangers,* was published by Parthian in 2015. markblayney.weebly.com

THE SIGNATURE OF GATES

NOVELLA EXTRACT BY **SAM LEWIS**

GEORGE HAD STARTED SQUATTING IN OTHER PEOPLE'S HOUSES AS A RESULT of her dreaming. She'd tested the waters to such an extent that each test had led her incrementally down a path that ended up with break-ins and a mild version of stealing. As a PhD student she'd allowed herself to dream, even though the dreams faded little by little as she approached the end of the funding. It was a project on phenomenology and Bunyan's Pilgrim's Progress: making the case that the religious pilgrimage was a way of embodying a desire to perceive. That the space between the beginning and the end of this spiritual stroll was a space of faith and that the longing to reach that enlightened state was exactly the same as the idea behind phenomenological intention: the process of perceiving things, of intending them into existence. All that, of course, didn't matter in the end. Proving that John Bunyan, a sixteenth-century Christian writer, was also a phenomenologist ended up ultimately a waste of three years. That's why George had had her nervous collapse. As with many of these catastrophic breakdowns, they happen slowly. They happen as gradually, but irreversibly, as the change of summer to winter.

And ultimately what was a PhD anyhow? Perhaps it was, as far as George could see, just another long-winded way to join a very privileged club? The main qualification to join this club seemed to be the ability to give no real shit about the research; to see it as a means to an end and ultimately use it cynically. Once her supervisors had begun to lose interest in Bunyan and focus on the dynamic types that researched genitalia in romantic poetry and so on, she started to drive her little battered Suzuki out to the nearby hills and walked in a kind of daze. On these walks she thought about her recent dreams. She hadn't bargained for the fact that these dreams might still exist, that by walking out here in the wild Welsh hills she was ignoring the reality that she now stood no chance of living in them. She walked defiantly for hours, ignoring the increasingly threatening emails from the department about deadlines and funding clawback. She knew that a dream of a steady university job and a little cottage in a charming village somewhere was very much a thing of the past. More and more she began to realise that jobs in universities were the preserve of a very shrewd few and that cottages of any sort were now the barracks of the wealthy.

Sometimes she stumbled across a darkened, often shuttered, little idyllic pad on the edge of a wild hill or deep forest and she'd pause. Her mind would turn to how it must be to live there. She peered into quarry-tiled rooms and noticed the thick velvet curtains. She'd imagine sitting on the upturned wrought iron chairs on little patios or decking areas. Perhaps she'd be quaffing a beer, with Radio Three piping in the background, while staring out at the unending and varied greens of all the remote and healthy valleys. She could imagine slow-cooking things, with shallots and red wine, and then eating in front of a blazing wood burner. If she lived in these places, she'd look at the chimney on a winter night and pinch herself at her luck, as little puffs of picture-postcard smoke would climb into the sky. Imagine this. She looked, as if from afar, at the meaning of these places; the meaning of a life there. The thick wooden doors, often painted a sage green, were always locked. The glass in the windows prevented her smelling the woodsmoke from the night before. She didn't live in Wales, she stayed in Wales.

Gradually she began to map the locations of these holiday cottages in her mind. She watched them from tree lines and rock outcrops, utilising her late father's powerful binoculars to study the walls, roofs and tracks. Occasionally she'd arrive at one of these observation outposts and see that the owners were there. This turn of events, which was actually rare even in the summer months, provided a tense mix of emotions. She felt the loss, projected as jealousy, as she watched these people fully indulging in the pleasures their little part-time pile gave them. She saw the kids racing around the lawns and the fathers proudly barbecuing on balmy evenings. She saw flutes of Cava and paperback books. She saw Volvos muddily defying their usual habitat, parked as they were on rutted tracks. Though this brought her some sadness, she also derived significant pleasure watching. Sometimes she liked to make predictions about what these people might do next; what their plan might be. But better still she felt almost euphoric at her prescience and their banality when they did exactly what she thought they would. Her sadness prevented her feeling uncontrolled hate towards them, but she certainly felt waves of resentment pass through her, forcing her to spit or make little gun shapes with her hands. She was in no doubt at all that these people were no better than her; it was only luck that separated them.

If she was certain that no one would be home, she started to take a few provisions to sit in the gardens. With her dwindling resources she'd buy a few delicate items from Marks & Spencer, usually along with a bottle of wine, and rearrange the seats in the garden to fully perform her dream-fuelled quasi residency. She might roll smoked salmon slices onto doughy French sticks and sip at decent Sauvignon Blancs. After lunching in the midday heat, with the insects humming around the hedges, she might take a post-prandial stroll around the grounds. Sometimes she would be so lost in her daydreaming that she'd try the front door on some sort of homing autopilot and be jolted back into her stark reality. With that she'd chug the rest of the booze and slope off to her car once the sun set to sleep on the cramped back seat.

Over time she noticed that generally the owners did not guard their houses well. They'd leave windows partially open and tended not to have the CCTV set-ups so popular with the retired Brummies that lived in elaborate bungalows in the area. She pondered this. For people who were clearly so materialistic, they seemed to have rather a blasé attitude as far as their vulnerable properties in the middle of nowhere were concerned. The only conclusion she could reach was that, in their arrogance, they assumed that it was impossible that anyone would violate them; that their privileges naturally extended to that of the local population, without so much as asking.

It didn't take long for the university to pull George's funding and, true to form, they announced this with a cruelty that can only be found in places that deal in ethics. Her trips to the hills had been costing her dearly and her fantasy lifestyle in the gardens of second homes hadn't helped matters. Her rent was overdue on the little studio annex in Aberystwyth she'd called home, so she made the rash decision to live in her tent. This was the only way she'd ever be able to wake up to the sounds of streams and birds or the views of big landscapes encased in pure air, she reasoned with a wounded logic. She told her mother what she planned to do, and she urged her to come home to the south of England. This was no solution, even though she'd be considerably more comfortable. She'd been working for three years on something no one cared about and had therefore added to her problems by rendering herself almost totally unemployable. In order to keep her daughter alive, her mother had insisted she give her one hundred pounds a week, which she could barely afford, but since her mind was in no condition to be anything but selfish, George accepted the offer willingly. At least for the summer, George could live the dream she couldn't shake, and perhaps by autumn be able to figure out what it was she was going to do with the rest of her life. She dumped the car in a layby and walked into the woods.

It had started well enough. There had been plenty of places to pitch up and very occasionally she'd find a spot that could do her for weeks.

She'd put up with snooty locals with unbridled dogs that would sniff and piss on her things, but she'd learnt quickly that charm could pay. Even though her clothing had quickly become grimy, her voice – a clear and articulate trill – could keep people at bay for some time. Certainly, she'd encountered some terminal resistance from foresters and rangers, but if she moved on quickly they didn't tend to hold a grudge. Despite her feral life being bearable, at times it got tiring and it was on one such occasion that she decided to force a window for the first time [....] With a small wiggle she was inside and standing in someone else's world, smelling them. She had made a transition from outside to in, from objective to subjective, with very little fuss. There was a cooker, a wood-burning stove, plates and chairs. She noticed a wine rack filled with bottles.

That night had turned into something of an epiphany. This was easy, relatively harmless, and seemed to be a way for one insignificant person to press some sort of wealth distribution button. How bad was this? At the end of the day, an empty house kept all of its wonders to itself; if the proper owners weren't enjoying them, surely they were being wasted? George had certainly taken advantage that night: drinking two bottles of mid-range red, cooking an excellent Waitrose ready meal she found in the freezer, sleeping in front of a broiling, roaring fire, and bathing at length in the large p-bath with all the attendant smells and lotions she could find.

In the morning she had pondered using the washing machine but had had her mind made up quickly when she heard a tractor merely a few fields away. Thankfully, the farmer had seemed intent only on 'checking the sheep', but it made George think a while. If she was going to do this on any regular basis, she'd have to establish a sort of best practice. She'd lock the door from the inside, check that the curtains were closed in the rooms she would use. She needed to make sure she didn't use any lights, but rely instead on candles and her headlamp. As she looked at her possessions strewn around the floor, spilling out of her large rucksack, she realised that if she was rumbled, she'd never be able to get out in time with her stuff. No, it was essential that she was permanently ready to run; packed and primed. Ownership was the only legitimate way to find that place of total relaxation and George had to accept that she could only enjoy half an experience of a rural home. Half would do for now.

Sam Lewis lives and works in Aberystwyth. He is an educator, and started creative writing during the recent lockdown. He focuses on the local landscape and the political and sociological tensions that exist there. This is an extract from Sam's entry, 'The Signature of Gates', which was placed third in the New Welsh Writing Awards 2023 Rheidol Prize for Prose with a Welsh Theme or Setting, judged by Gwen Davies this summer at Hay Festival. Sam wins a two-night stay at Gladstone's Library.

THANK YOU TO OUR #SECURENEWWELSHREVIEW SUPPORTERS

Diamond Supporters:
Mary Chadwick
Professor Tony Curtis
Mary Oliver
Kaite O'Reilly

Platinum Supporters:
Tasha Alden
Ruhi Behi
E Clifford Cutler
Jasmine Donahaye
Elaine Ewart
Katie Gramich

Kurt Heinzelman
Gareth Lewis
Rhiannon Lewis
Susan Merriman
Jackie Morris
Dr Chris W Pitt
Jim Pratt
Tracey Rhys
Amy Strange
Clive Upton
Roger Williams
Carole Hailey

THE VISITOR CENTRE

NOVELLA EXTRACT BY **PETE BARKER**

THE OLD STONE WALLS OF THE DESERTED HOUSE SHIVERED IN THE DARKNESS. Beyond them, wind-strewn sheep hunkered down in hollows between mountainside gorse and bracken. Snow started to fall. Not Christmas card, pretty snow but hard, stung with ice snow.

Who would be out in this weather, the evening drawing in as rapidly as a barn owl bearing down on its prey? People with things to do, places to be, that's who. The winter had been growing steadily colder, day by day, and life had to 'stay calm and carry on', ignore the consequences, just deal with front and centre, and that's how they ended up in this dire situation.

The farmhouse was deserted, then converted, and now it housed a natural and unnatural story of the land it sat firmly, resolutely and lost in the middle of. It housed the echo of voices, past and present, sliding under the slate roof, slipping between doors and snaking into the walls of a human mind.

The mind belonged to Rhys, or so he claimed: others would disagree. His was the voice that claimed the space on this descending evening, drifting in and out of the bare, cold rooms.

'Tum de tum,' it went. 'Hum de hum.'

'Rhys, what are you doing here? It's a bad night to be out.'

'Yes it is,' said Rhys, puffing his hollow chest out. 'But I'm in charge of the visitor centre, I need to be here.'

'*Yes, Rhys, you're in charge.*'

'Thank you for your vote of support. Now, if you would kindly keep the ghosts at bay, I will be deeply appreciative.'

'*Agreed. Are you staying all night, in case people want to drop in?*'

'A night like this, someone may need help, stranded in the snow. I'll handle things.'

He filled a kettle from a plastic five-litre container and lit the small camping gas stove.

'Cup of tea I think.'

'*Good idea, two sugars.*'

Rhys laughed as he dropped a tea bag in his mug but stopped at the sound from above his head. Footsteps, creaking their way across the old beams upstairs.

'Do you hear that?' Rhys asked.

'*I do.*'

'Sounds like someone is up there.'

'*I doubt it. I'll go and take a look if you like?*'

'Yes do that,' Rhys said. 'Let me know if you see anything.'

A few minutes later and Rhys is hovering over the small electric heater in the main room of the visitor centre, sipping his tea.

'Anything?' he asks.

'*No, nothing to worry about. Probably the cold making the boards creak: it's an old house.*'

'An old house,' Rhys repeated, 'full of relics.'

*

A single-pane window of the brick-walled shed rattled to the tune of the worsening weather, accompanied by a discordant draught forcing its way under the door and around the legs of the infantry section, who stood in rough formation before their sergeant and a flip chart. The lighting was poor but a wall lamp illuminated a large map behind the officer, partly turning him into a silhouette. Skulking in the shadows by the back wall were oversize backpacks and armaments.

'Exercise Nightingale will commence at 18.00 hours. The command post will be in The Drovers, as usual. You will be issued with live ammunition so, most important, full safety. We will be advancing through this valley and taking a position overlooking this plateau.' The sergeant was pointing at the map. 'Foster and Torio, you will make your way to the northern perimeter to this observation position.' He indicated a pinned note with a grid reference. 'You should find an old stone circle. We will be live firing across to an enemy position twenty metres south of target number four.' He leaned in for a closer study of the map. 'Ah, here... roughly. We will then move out south-east and RV with Six Platoon to receive further instructions. Any questions?'

'Sir.'

'Yes, Foster?'

'What do we do after you move out?'

'Stay in position until notified. You won't be needing live rounds either.'

Dave lowered his head. 'Sounds like a barrel of laughs.'

'What was that, Foster?'

'Nothing, sir.'

'Grab your kit,' barked the officer to the assembled soldiers, 'we're leaving in ten.'

Colin Torio made his way over to Dave Foster. 'Won't be so bad, piece of piss for us, just have to hang around all night.'

'Have you seen what it's like out there? I'd rather be marching than watching.' Dave hugged his shoulders for affect.

'It'll be alright, find ourselves a sheltered spot under some trees.'

'Trees? It's a barren plain.'

Colin went over to the map and pulled off the note with grid references. 'Look, pine plantation right next to us.' His fingernail scratched at the paper.

'C'mon, let's get our kit.' Dave started walking to the back of the room where the others were loading their rifles.

*

Tina was loading the dishwasher as Adam finished his phone call.

'Okay, thanks Jenny, I'll come over,' he said.

'Your dad?' Tina asked.

'Yeah, not looking good.'

He was standing, head bowed, in the kitchen doorway. She went over to put her arms around him but he held up a warning hand.

'Not now,' he said. 'I need to get over there.'

'But it's nasty out there, the forecast is more snow.'

'The roads are clear, I'll be alright.'

'Your sister can cope, you know.'

'I need to be there.'

'I understand,' she said.

He retreated to the hallway and gathered his Berghaus jacket off a rack. She followed him and also reached for her woollen coat.

'What are you doing?' Adam asked.

'Coming with you.'

'You don't have to.'

'I want to. If you're going, I'm going. I love your dad, I want to see him too.'

'What about the kids?'

'Sofi's old enough to look after Ben. We won't be long, will we?'

'No, not long.' Adam looked through into the lounge where the two children were absorbed in their screens. Ben lay on the carpet, his flop of fair hair covering his face, while Sofi, another blondie, with a button nose and chubby cheeks, hogged the brown leather sofa. Both playing games to the background accompaniment of a wide-screen TV looping music videos.

'Look, we'll put the portable heater in there for them so they won't get cold and Sofi can always call us if there's a problem.' Tina raised her voice, 'Won't you Sofi?'

'Yeah, what-evs,' came the reply.

Tina set up the heater and briefed Sofi as Adam picked up the keys to their ageing Ford and opened the door, through which Tina hurried, out into the blended light of snow-bright street lamps and late-afternoon sadness.

*

The young woman sat cross-legged on a deep crimson cushion in the middle of her room. Little could be seen in the dim light from a single purple candle and a glowing joss stick, its essence curling up to a thin fug of fragrance under a smoke-stained ceiling. The sound of a harp easing its way from an old-fashioned DVD player came to an end. She opened her eyes, took a deep breath and listened to the wind outside her window.

'Great Spirit save us,' she murmured to the crystal in her hand. She unfolded her legs and stood. The change of altitude made her reach for the dressing table. Steadied and adjusted to the dim surroundings, she adjusted her jeans, put out the candle and carefully placed the moldavite into a cedarwood box.

Descending narrow stairs, she swept aside the curtain at the foot and squinted in the bright light of the kitchen. Finding the dimmer switch, she turned down the LEDs and collected her phone from the table, checked for messages, nothing, threw it back, then over to the Aga to warm her hands.

Having resuscitated her digital circulation, she moved to the window; kneeling on the wide ledge, she gazed out across the white hillside. The light was fading but there was still work to do and she had been cooped up all day.

'Gonna check on the animals,' she called out to her father in the room next door.

'Be careful, Rhiannon, it's bloody cold out there. Take the quad.'

'Yeah will do,' she said, pulling on layers of coats and leggings.

Stepping into wellies by the back door and pulling gloves from her coat pocket, Rhiannon braced herself for the winter.

Once outside, the warmth of the kitchen stove forgotten, she strode across the yard to the open barn, past the quad bike and into the depths of the shed. She wheeled her Yamaha scrambler out onto the snow, jumped on and accelerated up the track, allowing the back to slide sideways in an exultant spray of icicles.

*

The flock lay hunkered in the lee of a small hazel copse in the bottom field, a hay bale pulled into threads nearby. Sheep farming was no longer viable but her father kept these on as a link to the past and for his plate, saying they tasted 'more real than the lab stuff'. Rhiannon refused to eat them. She did a quick head count: one missing. *Bugger,* she thought. If it's dead, she won't be able to sling it over her bike, should have brought the quad. She scanned the pasture for any white lumps that shouldn't be there and saw none in the diminishing light, so embarked on a slow tour of the perimeter. As she crested the crown of the field, a cold blast almost blew her off her bike. She pulled her woolly hat down further on her left, windward side, then carried on. She spotted the errant ewe in the far corner, head stuck in a wire fence as the animal reached for grass sheltered from the snow by a hedge. When Rhiannon pulled up, she could tell the sheep had been there some time and was weak but still it pushed and bucked against her efforts to free it. She was gripping it between her knees and pulling at the square embrace of wire when something caught her eye. Movement down by the bottom gate. She straightened up to get a better view. Someone was down there but disappeared behind the hedge, or even through the hedge? The sheep pushed harder into the fence with renewed energy, dragging Rhiannon's attention back. She tucked the ewe's ears back through and finally the face, releasing the animal. It ran off a short distance then turned back to watch Rhiannon.

'Go on you silly sod, go find your mates,' she said. The ewe didn't move. With a deep sigh, Rhiannon got back on her bike and, with a quick glance over to the bottom gate, slowly herded the animal back to the flock.

It was proper dark when she eventually returned to the warm farmhouse kitchen. She hung her sodden hat over the range and called out to her father.

'I'm back. One ewe stuck in the fence: did you not see her earlier?'

'No. Is she alright?'

'Think so, tucked in with the others now. It's minging out there.'

'Is Rhys still down at the visitor centre?'

'Guess so.'

'Tell him to come home will you.'

Rhiannon huffed. 'Can't you phone him?'

'Phone's not working. Line down I expect, with this weather.'

'So I've got to go back out there to fetch him?'

'Would you? Thanks love.'

Rhiannon pulled her waterproof leggings back on and grabbed her helmet. 'Feckin' Rhys,' she grumbled.

'What's that?'

'Nothing, Da.'

Pete Barker grew up in the seventies in a Dorset village and, in 1994, produced the history booklet, *East Lulworth Through the Ages*. He has published a novel, *System Error: Invitation to Revolution* and the narrative nonfiction book, *20 Riot Cops to Nick 2 Chickens: Climate Activists Reveal True Stories* (Dixi Books). His short stories include 'Wednesday's Child' (*Aftermath*) and 'Someone To Hold' (winner of the 2018 Flash 500 competition). Pete is a Greenpeace volunteer, and, with his wife, lives off-grid in mid Wales with seventeen rabbits and a cat. This is an extract from Pete's entry, 'The Visitor Centre', which was highly commended in the New Welsh Writing Awards 2023 Rheidol Prize for Prose with a Welsh Theme or Setting, judged by Gwen Davies this summer at Hay Festival.

THE LAST DAY BY OWAIN OWAIN

TRANSLATION PREVIEW FROM Y DYDD OLAF BY
EMYR WALLACE HUMPHREYS

I FIRST BECAME AWARE OF *Y DYDD OLAF*, OWAIN OWAIN'S POSTMODERN sci-fi masterpiece, like many others of my generation, through Gwenno's 2014 debut album of the same name. The album flew under my radar at the time; I only caught the tail end of her set at a London music festival in 2019 where she was promoting her excellent Cornish-language follow-up *Le Kov*. That snapshot was enough for her music to soundtrack the tube home, and the rest of my time in London, finishing my MA in Translation Studies at UCL and walking dogs to pay the rent.

Several months later, during the chaotic and terrifying first months of the pandemic, I found myself at my partner's house attempting to get my fledgling freelance translation career off the ground. I had recently crash landed in Wales from Brazil, where I was due to begin a literary translation course in São Paulo before the pandemic reared its head. I began receiving offers for Welsh translation work, despite not having used it substantially since my time at Ysgol Gyfun Penweddig over a decade previously. With nothing to lose, I decided to take on this work, and began reconnecting with the language and, by way, my identity: I enrolled in an online proficiency course with Dysgu Cymraeg, started speaking Welsh on the phone with my father again, and read several Welsh-language books by authors like Kate Roberts and John Gwilym Jones. *Y Dydd Olaf*, naturally, was on my reading list.

It's difficult to convey the experience of reading *Y Dydd Olaf* for the first – or any other – time. I think this is partly because it subverts many elements we take for granted in Welsh novels. We learn of the plot – of how swathes of the human race have been gathered, assimilated and 'stored' at the behest of a shadowy cybernetic authority figure – within the first few lines. Moreover, the final diary entry of protagonist Marc, which only survives for having been written in Welsh, comes at the beginning, and we spend the rest of the novel reading the preceding documents to learn how this nightmarish scenario came to be.

Y Dydd Olaf is surreally atemporal despite every document being dated, and the names of the town and university where much of the story is set are curiously absent. Instead, Owain conveys the story and its themes through minutiae: motifs such as curlews, blackberry jam sandwiches, cattle feed and shibboleths appear, reappear and recombine in various configurations to dizzying, claustrophobic effect.

There are meditations on free will, AI and subservience to technology throughout the novel's 120-odd pages. Most striking to me, on my fourth read-through, is its anti-war message, and discussions on what it means to be a linguistic and cultural minority as opposed to a racial one (a tension embodied by Cwansa and the attitudes towards his racial minority status exhibited by other characters).

It's commonly known that science fiction began to grapple with such concepts decades before gaining acceptance within the wider cultural sphere. Moreover, Welsh has a well-developed and complex literary tradition where the use of science fiction for discussing national identity was nothing new by the time the novel was written in 1968. However, reading it so many decades later, it is startling just how immediate (and sometimes uncomfortably on-the-nose) these discussions can be.

As Welsh society continues to articulate its identity in a postindustrial, post-Brexit and post-pandemic world, *Y Dydd Olaf* offers readers a space to learn how similar struggles were articulated nearly sixty years ago. While 'Yma o Hyd', Wrexham and Michael Sheen populate our screens and mark the Welsh on the digital landscape, official numbers of Welsh speakers and Welsh-identifying residents are decreasing. Wales in the digital age resounds with echoes from *Y Dydd Olaf* – I am very grateful to have just found in Parthian a publisher for the full-length English translation, and so, after all these years, more readers can hear those echoes too.

Prologue 1

READER, YOU SURELY KNOW THE STORY OF THE LAST DAYS OF THE PREVIOUS century (then known as the 'Twentieth Century') and how they heralded the present age on Earth. Now, ten years after those events, we have released these documents you hold in your hands. They are as unusual as they are important, for there is no way to truly comprehend them; there is a scarcity of information on the Lost Century, and we have no other primary resources to bridge us, the people of the present century, to those of the last. You surely know why.

Two works are frequently mentioned in the main body: *Brave New World* and *Nineteen Eighty-Four*. If we are to understand the references made to these books, then we may consider their loss one of the great tragedies of the Lost Century, especially in light of our efforts to establish its events.

The survival of these documents, which were compiled and bound anonymously, is nothing short of miraculous, and the rarest of gifts to us, believing as we do, the story of their preservation. We have endeavoured to release them in the order they were found (pay attention to their dates, reader):

- Entries from the Last Diary of the man named Marc;

- Miscellaneous documents from the final six months of the Twentieth Century;

- Entries from Marc's Early and Middle Diaries;

- Various miscellaneous correspondences in chronological order.

We, the Higher Committee of the New Few, have not altered this discovery in any way. However, for reasons that will become clear to you, we judged it wise to place the final entry of Marc's Last Diary in the next section as a second prologue, keeping earlier entries from the same day in their rightful place later on.

As previously mentioned, the original publisher of these documents remains anonymous. We must disclose, reader, that they made three major alterations: firstly, by including a translation; secondly, by placing them in the order described above and dividing them into two parts; finally, by including these words at the end:

Marc:
in praise and condemnation;
forgiveness, persecution;
for honour and derision.
I write in love and hate.
I knew; I never knew.

Marc's Last Diary: 1

01/09/99: AM

They tell me to write, but They don't know I'm not one of the Rest – They don't know about the platinum.

So I'll write! I'll write boldly, like I'll never be caught red-handed; satisfied, like one who's discovered the perfect's imperfections – and with the spirit of one who knows his work will live on in the future.

We had a warm welcome this morning, some two hours ago. Two whole hours in the Sunset House… and here's me writing 'this morning' as if those few minutes are already part of the distant past.

There was never any hope of escaping. That's part of Their cleverness. I came here just like the Rest – with a smile on my face, seemingly of my own accord. But what choice did I have? The slightest sign of failure would have caused a painstaking investigation – then that would've been the end.

At least here there's the certainty of another six months of life. There's the old saying where there's life there's hope; if what I heard before coming here is true, then there's still hope that I can transmit some part of this truth for the ages.

Yes, it looks like what I heard about the diaries is true. Here's the proof, in front of me now. But what about the other rumour, that the Computer-General has uninstalled the programme for translating sub-languages? I'll find out before long if that's true – tomorrow at the latest!

If so, some truth will be kept in the Computer-General's memory, for the future. If not… poor you, Marc!

If I had a glass of wine I would raise a toast to Omega-Delta, who (or what) ever they are! A long and healthy life to you, Omega-Delta! Keep at it – and long may you cause the Computer-General indigestion!

So easy to assimilate us! Even to me, one of the Few who know of the platinum, the Computer-General is more man than machine. He has a personality and even suffers from indigestion!

More man than machine, turning mankind into machines.…

Why is it we came here as false versions of well-rounded humans – of independent, sensitive, unique beings? Why the detailed planning, the complex, encyclopaedic sub-programmes, the elaborate assimilation systems, just to create this image of freemen walking merrily though the gates of the Sunset House?

Who does this please? Is it Them? Or the Computer-General himself? To what end?

Why do They need a false world full of free-willed human beings? Is it some echo of a primitive conscience which They once failed to assimilate? Or is it the Computer-General who demands this fake free world and people – in that case, why and what for? Is there a material, physical or electronic worth to a fantasy of this kind? Does the 'de-humaniser' himself need a false human world in order to guarantee the effectiveness of his plans?

I know we're in the Sunset House because of our 'resources'. I know the aim of the next six months is to enrich those 'resources'. I know we are raw material – to create life according to Their definition. If that's the case, I wonder if it's because sustaining life – of any kind– is impossible without a 'freedom' of some sort? That's it: perhaps Their 'life' depends on our 'freedom', whether fake or not.

But I don't really know. This, above all else, is the ultimate mystery.

Yes, we were warmly welcomed. Strange to think that even They still insist on using the symbolic act of the handshake.

The feeling of Their skin was so unnatural. Human skin, once upon a time. It's likely the Rest, my platinum-less neighbours on Lv3, never noticed how unnatural it felt.

Noticed? Does any 'noticing' happen among the Rest anymore? Are their actions not just a series of conditioned reactions by now?

Of course, the unnatural skin of the hands which greeted us, the residents of Lv3, didn't trigger any negative sensations or reactions in the

Rest. There is no command in their assimilation files that reads EVENT: TOUCH OF SKIN. REACTION: UNNATURAL SENSATION EVENT SYMPTOMS. They cannot react negatively to the touch.

The touch of skin on skin. This morning, to me, I felt a jolt in that touch.

The jolt of fear, perhaps?

Twice – many years ago, before the present system took over – did I experience such a thing.

Once was with Mam. The last touch of my lips against her forehead. The jolt of fear? No, not fear. No emotion of any kind (though isn't the absence of all emotion itself an emotion?). Nothing. No reaction, no recognition. No nothing. That's why I felt such a jolt: just the utter, utter lack of reaction. Skin, totally unaware of the touch of skin. No sensation. No empathy. No chill from the cold, either. Just empty, unfeeling distance. The disconnected isolation from that awful proximity. Touching without touch; close, close, and the gulf in between so infinitely massive. And that profound jolt, the perfect negation of every one to ever come before – from my mother's first touch to her last moments of unknowing – electrifying the skin.

The first time was with Anna, at school. In the perfection of first touch. A simple event: borrowing a book. Our fingers touching, perhaps by accident. Skin kissing skin in total innocence for a split second – the slightest moment. And that simple touch paralysing my whole body with a torturous, totally real, jolt.

Back then, I knew my feelings for Anna. Did she know? Back then, or any time?

It's hard to believe she didn't know. Hadn't that electricity been coursing through her body too? Didn't our shared consciousness create it?

There was an echo – echoes – a handful of times afterwards. Each one different. The shock of discovering what I'd been imagining all the while – yes, her skin was pale and smooth and warm and alive. And the shock of discovering what I had never imagined: that the intertwining of bodies is not only a physical act.

How did you forget all this, Anna? *Did* you forget? And if you did, how can you explain –

No, I'm rambling. Trespassing. This is not my task. What benefit to the future is there in these half-baked attempts at interpreting old experiences with partial and inaccurate information?

Control yourself, Marc – do what little there is to do in the time you have.

Very well. I'll write, not note; remember, not reminisce. This is all for you, unknown reader – I know nothing of your era, your race; and I cannot even imagine your hopes and dreams.

Today, six months before the end of the twentieth century, in the year of our Lord nineteen ninety-nine. Our Lord? Do you know of our Lord in your time?

It's so difficult getting the truth onto the page! Where to start? What to explain? What secrets have we got today that are common knowledge in your time? What obvious truths do we have which are total mysteries to you?

We live on a planet we call Earth. Is this something you knew? In the days of the Council of Fraternities – and the Computer-General – and Them. And the Rest, of course. And the Few – Pedr, myself and the few others who know of the platinum.

Do you know of free will? You know more than I do if so! But really – like me, you must have at least some idea of what it means. Looks like it's lost forever on the Rest, but I'm not totally sure. It was conquered by their assimilation, then finally annihilated by their assimilation ray.

And Them? It's difficult – even impossible – to say. They still have some free will, perhaps – sometimes. Lord only knows!

Only we – the Few – possess what I understand to be free will. There are a hundred of us, perhaps, on the face of the Earth. And there are times when the platinum loses its effect – when our thoughts wear the synthetic language of the Council of Fraternities, trespass on forbidden ground and attract the assimilation ray, full power, into our heads. It makes one go temporarily mad.

Remember this, reader: it's not always me who's writing. Sometimes it's obvious. Others, it's impossible to tell.

Please! For your own sake, I must show you. I'll start thinking, using the artificial syntax, of the Computer-General – the man-machine, the font of the Spirit of Fraternity, trying to understand the relationship – forbidden – still thinking in this synthetic language – my thoughts trespassing – the pain is starting – the ray– don't read – must write – don't fratolish hiang perpetshki

fratolish hiang perpetshki

fratolish of course Anna's different nobody but Anna knows Pedr doesn't know hiang perpetshki

fratolish hiang only hope Omega-Delta's messenger who are they? sabotage plans perpetshki

fratolish hiang perpetshki

fratolish the clock on campus says nine o'clock hurry Pedr Siwsan and Mari are coming where's Cwansa will you call for Cwansa give his wall a knock Pedr hey Cwansa give hiang perpetshki

hiang perpetshki

fratolish hiang I can't refuse that Aunt just a little something I got five pounds from her once of course I will Aunt it's worth five pounds nearly said my pleasure to her lordy I best perpetshki

fratolish hiang perpetshki

fratolish hiang perpet Mam Mam but she isn't answering I don't know why jam sandwich lovely tea Mam Mam is that her there of course who else but that's not Mam either ye no ye no shut your mouth and show some respect perpetshki

fratolish hiang Anna Anna Anna pale and slender and slender and pale and no one but Anna knows what happened in the meeting perpetshki

fratolish Cwansa's black Cwansa's God's black is the Computer-General black to Cwansa how he's black hiang perpetshki fratolish hiang perpetshki fratolish Siwsan Siwsan Siwsan Siwsan Siwsan Siwsan Siwsan Siwsan Siwsan hiang perpetshki

fratolish hia They're making tasty blackberry jam full of tasty maggots with a tasty curlew with Lv2 and Lv4 and drinking coffee in the Twb but the Computer-General doesn't want blackberries nor maggots nor coffee he eats lives not loaves perpetshki

fratolish hiang perperperperperperperper

Marc's Middle Diary: 1

05/01/1984

It's too late – for me, and the rest of the Few. There's no way to stop the Council. We missed the chance. It's all-consuming now. There is nothing we can do. Very soon (a few days perhaps?) they will begin the final phase, and we won't be able to stop it.

It's obvious that Cwansa is no longer one of us – in any way whatsoever. It's better to believe that than to believe he still doesn't know how far things have gone, and for how long. Anna absolutely knows but doesn't want to admit it. Why didn't she tell him before it got too far?

Puppet or not, Cwansa's influence was still strong until very recently – and his line of work allowed him to exert it. Why didn't he act? Did he not realise he had to?

When should one cut the rot from the flesh? How does one decide when's best to swap the knife out for balm? Can one be overly forgiving? Can forgiveness turn into resentment? What then? Did we conflate forgiveness with cowardliness, and were we aware of this or not? Were we afraid of the rot, the evil seed cast in our own flesh, and taking to it with a razor blade?

Is it possible to condemn, punish and forgive someone, all at once?

For the Almighty perhaps, but not mankind. Not me, at least. If I condemn someone and call for their punishment, then I wouldn't be strong enough to forgive them as well. Not really – just a shadow of forgiveness: bitter, empty, hypocritical.

But I must learn to forgive Cwansa, stop condemning him and any attempt to punish him. Who am I to judge him, then deny him forgiveness? But that's the case with Cwansa, where love isn't clouding my senses – how could I possibly condemn Anna, and call for her punishment?

I don't know the truth; whether they're guilty or innocent, there is no way I'll ever know.

And if they're both guilty, don't ask me to be judge, jury and executioner.

Letter from Anna: 5

09/01/1984

My dear Marc,

By the time you get this, it will of course be too late, but no matter. Weren't you too late years ago? In school, whenever you borrowed a pencil or a book or some other random thing? In the Winllan, as we ran from ourselves? In the Twb, drinking the coffee we obviously weren't enjoying? On the campus lawn? The years we lost contact?

I'm writing, despite all this, to thank you. You gave me so much. You gave everything except one thing, the one thing I desired more than anything: your love. You never understood me, Marc. Or if you did, then you didn't understand love.

You kept your love, the one thing I desired most, from me – then you cursed me with Cwansa's.

Why did you ever introduce us? Why did you place that burden on me? Did you believe... no, it's not my place to try and understand you from your past actions.

I know you reject my explanation for what happened at the last Fraternity meeting. Be that as it may: you alone have the choice – to believe me or not. We'll never see each other again after today. At least, Marc and Anna won't.

Today is the end, Marc. The end of love, and so the end of everything. I only ever experienced love twice in my life: Cwansa's for me – and mine for you.

Anna.

Marc's Middle Diary: 4

10/01/1984

It's over.
I chose an hour ago, along with the other Few.
They still haven't found out about the platinum.
No letter from Pedr – nor anyone else.
My last words before
They're here. I hear them.
No time. Hiding this.
We fight.

Marc's last diary:14

01/09/99: PM

Fratolish hiang perpetshki

fratolish hiang perpetshki

fratolish hiang perpetshki

ubi-umgobo hiang perpetshki

ete-umgobo hiang perpetshki

hemi-umgobo hiang perpetshki

al computerex

al computerex

al computerex

fratolish hiang perpetshki

fratolish hiang perpetshki

fratolish hiang perpetshki

anak perpetshki

quanak perpetshki

computerex perpetshki

Owain Owain (1929–1993) was a writer, physicist and language activist. He founded *Tafod y Ddraig*, the Welsh Language Society newspaper which remains a cornerstone of Welsh-language activism, as well as creating the ubiquitous 'Dragon's Tongue' logo. A prolific and eclectic writer, his fictional biography, *Mical* (1976, Gomer), won Literature Wales' Book of the Year award. His novel, *Y Dydd Olaf,* was the inspiration for musical artist Gwenno Saunders' 2014 album of the same name. Since then, it has been translated into Polish and Cornish, and was republished in Welsh in 2021 by Gwasg y Bwthyn.

Emyr Wallace Humphreys translates from Welsh and Portuguese to English, and from English to Welsh. A graduate of the MA programme in Translation Studies at University College London, he has had literary translations published in journals such as *The White Review, Your Impossible Voice* and *Joyland Magazine*. In 2022 he was awarded a bursary to attend the Bristol Translates literary translation summer school, and was a Visible Communities mentee for the National Centre for Writing's 2022–23 Emerging Translator Mentorship programme. He was nominated for Deep Vellum's Best Literary Translations 2024 anthology. This is a preview from Emyr's full-length translation of Owain Owain's *Y Dydd Olaf*, to be published as *The Last Day* by Parthian in 2024.

IT'S HARD TO HEAR

the sonographer through her mask,
I can't see a heartbeat so easily mistaken

for *I can see her feet.* A moment
of delight before I see the shock

of cold gel darkening the waistband
of your jeans, your eyes fixed

on the quiet screen. Earlier, a nurse
called out for Rebel Fury

and someone's grandma left the blue line
of seats. *We should name our baby*

Rebel Fury, I said, palming the precious
swell of your belly. When the notice

board caught up and alerted
Beryl Drury to Room F7 –

Remember how we laughed,
waiting to be called in?

ONLY ACCESSIBLE BY WATER

Shipped off on a rented paddleboard.
    My married friends lick each other's
        ice-creams on shared beach towels,

shrinking as I am steered east
    along the coast by a man I've known
        for less than ten minutes. His shadow

trails in the water. My legs, dangling
    bait. *There are no sharks in Portuga*l,
        he grins, then splashes me with his

paddle. We drift through a rugged arch
    into Benagil, the famous sea cave
        on his post-divorce bucket list.

He takes photos on his GoPro
    of a seagull circling the blue eye
        above, asks if he can kiss me.

There are no boat tours. Only the rising tide,
    the single life-jacket between us,
        salt hardening on my string bikini.

Carson Wolfe (they/them) is a Mancunian poet. They are New Writing North's 2023 Debut Poetry Winner and have previously won awards from the Aurora Poetry Prize and the Button Video Contest. Their debut poetry pamphlet *Boy(ish) Vest* (2022) was praised by Dr Kim Moore as an 'unforgettable, wild, risk-taking roller-coaster of a book'. Their work has appeared in *Rattle, Fourteen Poems, Poetry by Chance* (Button, 2023), and *The Penn Review*. Carson lives in Manchester with their wife and three children. You can find them at carsonwolfe.co.uk.

UNSEASONAL

Rain fell like news you can do nothing
about: each morning a line of clouds

at the horizon swelling into turbulence
the streets glazed and cleansed, the river

bellowing where the bridge chokes it.
Then on Christmas Eve everything gilded

by low sun, jackdaws clacking in gangs
as they do after the solstice; starlings

ghosting the fields their shadow shrinking
and growing; a pair of buzzards spiralling

with pale underwings, the fells soaring
under them. Listen. Things are beginning

again, the birds waking at dawn, the light
renewing before the old year has properly

slipped away. We speak on the phone and
you're laughing in the old way, saying how

you turned up on your boxer-twin for the
scan, dangling your helmet, pissed through

by West Yorkshire rain. You've got a
tumour now. You talk about it as if it's

a surprising child, a prodigy, a wunderkind
there in the manger of your body, just

below the heart, your voice curious
and soft, as if it's sleeping now.

MOLES

You've got to love the way moles
get to it – as soon as the ground has

thawed and snowdrops are nodding
their heads above them – throwing

up a line of formidable earthworks
(an Englishman's home being his etc)

motorway straight, sometimes following
the line of a wall, sometimes joining

bunkers on a golf course or tossing
up heaps on the cricket square

between bowling crease and popping
crease. All good, the work of those

workaholics seems to say. All good
in the scheme of things like an

umpire watching a batter ask for
middle-and-leg; a lollipop lady

ushering kids across the road; like
navvies in their napped trousers

and waistcoats watching the first
pint being pulled. All good.

All in a night's work.

Graham Mort is emeritus Professor of Creative Writing at Lancaster University. His latest poetry book is *Black Shiver Moss* (Seren, 2017). A new book of poems, 'Rivers Joining', is in preparation. graham-mort.com

SISTER DORA ARRIVES IN WALSALL

1865

Her first thought — it is alive,
a great palpitating body of land
fused with machine, its multiple arms
pulling and reeling cages of men
up and down mine shafts,
hacking away at coal and clay;
another two hundred hands
cutting and stitching and staining
and polishing leather saddles;
another hundred hands filling furnaces,
stirring the amber glare of molten iron,
pouring, hammering, stamping.

Every furnace is a vivid red mouth,
sputtering sparks of fire. All day, all night,
the city coughs up filthy black fumes,
the skin of every brick grimed with bile.
Canals ooze gallons and gallons of sweat.

The two-roomed hospital in Bridge Street
has fourteen beds. It lies close
to a buckle factory. At every bang,
the bed-frames shiver, shiver, shiver.

Laura Stanley is the third-prize winner in Super Mario, Fidget Spinners & Beyoncé: The Pop Culture Poetry Challenge on Young Poets Network, and commended in Our Whole Lives, We Are Protest: A Poetry Challenge Inspired by the People of 1381, set and judged by Vanessa Kisuule in 2022.

THE LEGEND OF SISTER'S ARM

We day think it cud be dun.
Another poor mon wi' a twisted arm.
The doctor wanted it gun.

'Save me arm,' the poor man cries, 'it's me right wun.'
But the doctor says, 'If I dough take it, you'll die.'

'Ar car goo to the werkhouse,' the man cries.
'Please, save me arm.'
Sister Dora calls back: 'I'll try.'

The doctor leaves in a storm.
Says er's a barmy wench.
Er car save the poor mon from harm.

Sister looks after the poor mon's arm.
She cleans the stench
day and night for three wick term.

We day think it cud be dun.
But the poor mon stops his cries.
Sister takes the bandages off wun by wun.

The doctor looks at Sister's Arm.
'Bostin,' he replies.
All thanks to ower Dora's charm.

This poem is written in an imitation of the Walsall dialect, also known as 'yam yam'.

THE RIVERFLY CENSUS

The towpath's overhung with cow parsley and grasses,
weeping willows bend to the water. The day vibrates with flies –
fish break the surface for them, reflections readjust for them.
Mayflies spin across the river, midges spiral into columns
over water meadows that stretch towards another place.
I wave horse flies from my legs. It's the warmest May
and it hasn't happened yet, the time without flies.
The man I love hums. We look for somewhere to lie down.

UNDER THE HUT

Neighbours' cats were first to Mum's garden,
starlings took the attic above her room.
We watched them fledge.
A gang of sparrows occupied a bush,
a fox explored the kitchen one afternoon,
a herring gull used the cat flap for percussion.
Don came with his old dog,
the fox was replaced by a younger one,
a sparrow hawk dived at the gang and failed,
pigeons squatted in birdbaths.
The garden went wild that summer.

Tendrils of clematis, bindweed, rambling rose
caught on twigs and stems, the lavender spread,
grasses grew long and waved at us.
One night badgers discovered space below the hut,
dark as a car park, fenced in with wire.
They dug a hole like a whirlpool.
Excavations of chalky earth drowned the cat statue,
Buddha, smothered the blue petals of a plant
I always forget the name of. The hole suggested
tunnels and nesting chambers that can extend metres,
it's said, some occupied for decades.

At the borders of the excavation, their latrine,
a Magnolia Stellata that refuses to blossom,
dahlias attempting to defy all disturbance.
But the path is no longer a path
and our repeated conversations about family grow longer –
her questions, my answers disperse

in the way feathers do or burst out of us
like seeds. Sometimes they taste of ash,
smell of windfalls fermenting under apple trees.

Jackie Wills has published six collections of poetry, the most recent being *A Friable Earth* (Arc, 2019), and a handbook on reading and writing, *On Poetry: Reading and Writing Poems* (Smith|Doorstop, 2022). She has also published short stories, and has been a journalist and trade union activist. She received a Cholmondeley Award this year. Having run numerous reading groups and writing workshops, she now spends most of her time on her allotment or making/mending clothes on a casual basis, in order to lower her carbon footprint. Her family has deep roots in Wales but she lives in Brighton. jackiewillspoetry.blogspot.com/